See You Soon

Written by
Dilraz Kunnummal

Pictures by
Illustrations Hub

Edited by
Aditi Wardhan Singh

ISBN number : 9 789354 163760
www.mommydil.com

Dedication

For my lil ray of 'son'shine, my Ayan...

For everyone who has been the wind beneath my wings: my brilliant family and friends who became family (you know who you are).

For the brave Mama bears who love deeply and dream fiercely,

and their tribes which empower them to live passionate lives that are seemingly impossible...

Most importantly, for little ones everywhere who miss Mommy when she is away.

Come join us, as our little champ shows you everything is going to be okay.

A big hug and a kiss.

"Bye bye, my baby; I love you so much."
"See you soon," said Mama, as she went away.

When Mama works, I play and learn.
looked after by those who adore me -
teachers, grandparents or my nanny.

Some days, I spend my time with granny and gramps.
Yummy ice cream, giant hugs and taking turns on the swings.

Some days, I stay with my nanny.
She kisses my booboos, and wipes my tears – taking such good care of me.

Mama is not with me right now,
and that's alright.
I know she loves me more than words can say.

We both cried when she first waved bye,
but slowly, she and I learnt to be fine.
I was scared that she might forget me,
but she always came back at the end of the day.

I miss my Mama a lot,
but she makes me very proud.
Always being the best that she can be.

My friends and I love to talk about Mommy,
and to share stories about how awesome she is.
"What does she do?" my teacher asked.

"Mine is a doctor," said Emily.
"My Mom volunteers at the shelter," said Antonio.
"My mother is a chef," said Tiana.

"My Mommy is a lawyer," said Jamal.
"My Ma does research," said Radha.
"My Mama is an engineer," said Ang.

"Wow! They are all super Moms, and super amazing" admired the teacher.
"They are fierce, and strong and oh so lovely,
each wonderful in their own way."

"Some go to a workplace while others stay at home.
Wherever they are, every Mama works very hard,
and you mean the world to your Mama," our teacher comforted us.

Some days, I still feel sad when Mama has to drop me off.
But playing with my friends always cheers me up.
We build blocks, race cars, and cook on our kitchen set.

At the nursery, we enjoy learning together.
Circle time, splish-splash and getting messy with paints too.

Mama may be busy, but I am always on her mind.
I cannot wait for her to get here.
Mama and me - we make the best team.

When she comes in through the door, I run to her with glee.
Her face gives me joy. I make her heart smile.

We are a family.
But there are many others too.

Helping hands that support us,
keeping me safe and happy,
cheering as Mama reaches for the sky.

We eagerly wait for the holidays,
full of excitement, and heaps of cuddles,
fun and laughter from morning to night.

Giggles, and tickles and dancing away,
being so silly, till the moon shines bright

A big yawn, a snuggle and a bedtime story.
"Goodnight, sleep tight, my darling child," said Mama.
"Close your eyes, and dream of wonders tonight.
I love you today, tomorrow, and ever after."

"I love you too, Mama," I say.
I close my eyes and fall asleep,
eager to see what tomorrow brings.

A big hug and a kiss.

Tips

Here are some tips to get you through the big change:

💙 **Build Excitement and Familiarity:** Start talking to your little one about the childcare arrangements early, and share happy positive stories ("You will make new friends; you will have so much fun"). Visit the nursery early, have interactive sessions with the nanny or hang out with the grandparents. Try to do some of the activities that they may do when you are eventually away.

💙 **Be Calm on the First Day:** Children can sense your emotions. It is crucial that you stay calm and even smile while saying goodbye. Establishing a simple routine prior to the first day will definitely be beneficial.

💙 **Manage your expectations:** Realize that this is a new experience for you, and for your little one. Allow some time for your child to settle down, and know that there will be some amount of tears and fussiness for the first few days. As long as your little one settles down, and is happy soon after you leave, you can rest assured that they are in safe hands.

💙 **Focus on Connection:** Reiterate the fact that you love them, and that you will be back. Acknowledge their feelings and give a big hug while reassuring them that you will come to get them. Tell them you will be back at a specific time, or after a particular activity. This will help in allaying any fears your little one may have.

💙 **Remember the big picture:** You have your own very valid reasons to go back to work and to opt for a childcare provider. Remind yourself that these reasons are absolutely important, and that you have come to this decision only after giving it due thought. You are doing what is best for your family.

All the best..

"The single, most heartbreaking moment for a mom is when she has to leave a crying, clinging child with a care provider and walk away to get to work...It never gets easy..."

Mommy Dil

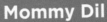

For Dilraz Kunnummal, one of the toughest aspects of motherhood was dropping off her little one to the nursery and returning to work, when her wee boy was only two months old. And her own personal experiences are her inspiration for 'See You Soon'

Apart from being Mama Bear, she is a journalist with experience across media platforms including print, television and radio; a dancer, choreographer, public speaker, Mom blogger, and more! Having been an expatriate throughout her life, she aims to tell stories, which are multicultural and can connect to a global audience. She has also contributed to a number of anthology books.

Tag @mommydil on instagram or FB, and share a review or reading of the book with the #SeeYouSoon, to get activity sheets sent to you.

I would also truly appreciate it if you can leave a review on Amazon for this budding author.
Thank you so much,
Love, Dilraz.

"Thank you for reading 'See You Soon', we hope you enjoyed it..

We would also truly appreciate it if you can leave a review on Amazon for this budding author.

Thank you so much.

See You Soon

Written by

Dilraz Kunnummal

Pictures by

Illustrations Hub

Edited by

Aditi Wardhan Singh

Contact@raisingworldchildren.com